**What Christians
Should Know About...**

Depression, Anxiety, Mood Swings and Hyperactivity

G.W. Mullen M.D.

Sovereign World

ISBN: 1 85240 210 5

SOVEREIGN WORLD LIMITED
P.O. Box 777, Tonbridge, Kent TN11 9XT, England.

Typeset and printed in the UK by Sussex Litho Ltd, Chichester, West Sussex.

Contents

Introduction

This booklet has been published to help Christians better understand the most common medical conditions that affect thinking and feeling. Christians are often very confused about the nature and treatment of mental illness. They are also very suspicious of psychiatric treatments, so many are suffering needlessly from correctable conditions.

This booklet will explain all the psychiatry that you need to know to remove the mystery, misunderstanding, confusion and stigma attached to the Mood Disorders, namely, Depression and Manic Depression. Hyperactivity and other common mental conditions will also be discussed.

The following pages will answer the most common questions that I've been asked in my Mental Health Clinic. You will then be able to recognize and understand these conditions and know how to get help. You will have the tools to help yourself or a suffering loved one return to normal functioning. You will also be better able to support someone going through the treatment process by giving them a reason to be hopeful.

Medical research in recent years has provided physicians with very effective tools to treat these common conditions. These treatments however, are not reaching the people who need them because of the lack of awareness and misunderstanding of the general public.

The current situation is similar to the era when eye glasses were first introduced. They were a very effective treatment for blurred vision but they were not well received by the public since people had no idea that they themselves had blurred vision and could be helped with glasses. Most had learned to live with their poor vision and ridiculed those who did wear glasses. Those who tried the glasses couldn't believe the improvement and wished that they had started wearing them years before. Their vision became normal but they had to live with the stigma attached to wearing glasses.

Now we are dealing with problems of "blurred" thinking, which are invisible to an observer. Even the sufferer doesn't know that he is not thinking as clearly as he should be. The victim is so accustomed to this disability that he doesn't think he needs help. He is then resistant to the suggestion that he could be helped and even ridicules those who do go for help. This booklet will allow anyone to "measure" their thinking pattern and determine if there is any "blurring" which could be corrected. This information of course, does not replace a proper evaluation by a physician or counsellor but it will assist in the evaluation process.

1

How Common is Depression?

Depression is one of the most undiagnosed and disabling medical conditions in society today. It costs the U.S. economy $27 billion annually in medical costs, lost productivity, unemployment, increased susceptibility to illness, suicide, family disruption, relationship failure, alcohol abuse and personal suffering. The Canadian costs are estimated at $5 billion annually. Only heart disease causes comparable disability and cost to society.

Depression is more disabling than most chronic illnesses. Even though there are now very effective treatments available, most people with depression remain undiagnosed and untreated due to lack of awareness and not accepting depression as a legitimate illness. The unnecessary suffering often continues for a lifetime, causing intense mental, emotional and physical anguish. It disrupts all relationships both at home and work.

If a person acknowledges this condition and goes for help, they then must endure the unfair stigma of an uninformed public that presumes that depression is a character defect, lack of will power or a personal weakness. Not only does a depressed person have to cope with the illness but also with the scorn of society. No other chronic illness is treated so unfairly by the public.

Six to ten percent of the population is depressed at any given time. This very common condition is undiagnosed and untreated in eighty per cent of its victims. Ten to twenty percent of women and five to ten percent of men will suffer from depression at some point in their lives.

Depression is more common in women due to poorly understood genetic factors. It is also more common as people age. It is found in all races and social classes. It even occurs in those who are not stressed and are otherwise completely well.

All disorders of mood are strongly inherited. A person has a tripled risk if there is one close relative with a mood disorder.

Depression is not a benign illness. Fifteen percent of untreated depressed people will commit suicide and eighty percent of all those who commit suicide have a treatable mental illness.

At least ten percent of the population will suffer from a mood disorder at some time in their life. Most will not be treated due to the stigma attached to the diagnosis and treatment. Stigma is the single most important obstacle to treatment. Sufferers are afraid to report their symptoms due to the negative consequences which may come in their work and family as a result of their diagnosis.

Effective treatment will only begin when a person recognizes the problem and overcomes the obstacles to treatment. Through public education, awareness of these conditions should increase and the stigma attached to these illnesses should dissolve.

2

How can one tell Depression from Discouragement?

Depression is by far the most common form of mental suffering. It is however, a poorly defined condition which means different things to different people. We must be able to distinguish between the transient "depression" of someone unhappy about a recent disappointment and the severe crushing despair of one who has for many years lost all interest in life. I choose to use the term "discouragement" for temporary mood fluctuations which would be commonly referred to as the "blues" and would never be considered an "illness". "Depression" is reserved for prolonged disorders of mood which require professional help.

It is not always easy to distinguish between these two conditions and it requires considerable training and experience. There is presently no blood test or X ray that will diagnose mental illness. Understanding what a person is thinking and feeling is the only way to separate these conditions.

Mood Control Centre

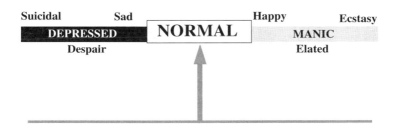

Figure 1 The Mood Control Centre should maintain mood in the normal range regardless of circumstances.

Discouragement is transient with an obvious cause and the person is still able to enjoy other unrelated activities. It resolves with time and supportive counselling. A discouraged person can still be hopeful, with good thought control and concentration.

Depression is usually very prolonged with unrelenting symptoms. It is often, though not always characterized by sadness. There is an inability to enjoy activities and all interests fade. There is general hopelessness and a lack of ability to control or steer thoughts. This is a much more disabling condition than discouragement. A more complete list of symptoms can be found in Chapter Four.

3

What causes Depression?

It is important to realize that forming a thought is as physical an event as blinking an eye or moving your arm. Nerve cells in the brain allow you to form thoughts in the same way that they permit movement. We only have full control of our thoughts when all the nerve cells are working properly to give us that control. This process is subject to malfunction like any other part of the body.

The brain is divided into regions or "control centres" that direct every activity of the body. The mood control centre (see Figures 1 and 2) is responsible for maintaining normal mood, which allows you to be relaxed, content, feeling in control, concentrating normally, clear headed and coping with stress. There are very specific chemical substances called neurotransmitters which are produced by brain cells to regulate these body functions. If anything happens to disrupt the production of these chemicals, then the control centre will malfunction and symptoms or disability will result.

If for example, brain cells malfunction in the movement control centre, then you will have difficulty with movement. A stroke is an example of this kind of disability. If the malfunction is in the mood control centre, then mood begins to fluctuate outside of your control or it slides into a depression which will not lift.

It is now well established that mental illnesses are usually the result of an imbalance in the chemicals associated with mood control. This tendency to malfunction is usually inherited. Symptoms may just appear without reason or depression may come as a result of stressful circumstances that bring out the inherited tendency to have a mood disorder. As a result of the discovery of the above facts, depression is now seen as a physical illness needing and responding to medical treatment.

Due to the genetic nature of the condition, a triggering stress is not always needed. Sometimes depression just develops over years with no obvious cause, much like diabetes. There is no doubt however, that stress can trigger a depressive illness in someone who already has the genetic potential for depression. If there is very strong genetic potential, then it will take very little stress to trigger an illness. If the genetic link is weaker, then more stress is needed to cause disability.

The treatment of depression is the same whether or not it was triggered by stress. If the chemical imbalance is present, it can be treated regardless of the cause. Think of it this way. If someone breaks their leg, they will need a cast. It doesn't matter if it was caused by a fall or a car accident, the treatment of the resulting disability is the same.

When the chemical imbalance is corrected, the person is then better able to deal with their stresses, usually with the help of a counsellor.

Brain Control Regions

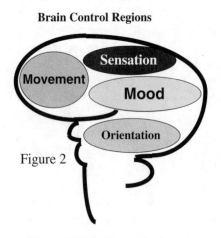

Figure 2 Brain Control Regions.

4

What are the symptoms of Depression?

Depression has a very wide variety of symptoms and each individual shows a different pattern. Generally speaking, these people usually have been sad for prolonged periods without obvious cause. They have lost interest in most activities of life which previously gave them pleasure. They feel defeated, useless, hopeless, unable to pray, punished by God, and unworthy of anyone's love or God's forgiveness. They may feel that God has left them or is no longer listening to them due to unknowingly committing the "unpardonable sin". They consider themselves to be a failure as a Christian and as a person. Plagued by guilt, they condemn themselves for not being able to "snap out of it". Some have increased irritability and will attack everyone around them as the likely cause for their unhappiness. They find it hard to relax or ever feel content. There is a diminished interest in sex or any kind of intimacy.

Depressed people often have great difficulty falling asleep due to persistent and uncontrollable racing of unpleasant thoughts or worries through their mind. Many will awaken at four a.m. and will be unable to fall asleep again because of the same racing of thoughts. Others oversleep and use it as an escape from an unpleasant reality.

Concentration on work, pleasure or reading becomes impossible while struggling with the continuous stream of unpleasant and depressing thoughts which cannot be kept out of the mind. When reading they will see the words but have to reread the sentence many times before understanding what was said. It is hard for them to keep their minds on anything. Their memory seems to fail and it becomes very difficult to finish any project due to fatigue or lack of interest.

Fatigue becomes overwhelming in eighty percent of depressed people. Daily responsibilities which were previously easy and pleasant are seen as enormous undertakings. Everything becomes such an effort that all activities are avoided. A depressed person also finds it very hard to make decisions since their self confidence is so low and concentration is so impaired. Anxiety becomes a continuous thought pattern which cannot be turned off. The depressed person will worry about everything, even tiny details of life which never before attracted their attention. Fifty percent of depressed people can't stop worrying. Intense fear and worry may induce unusual behaviour patterns like repetitive hand

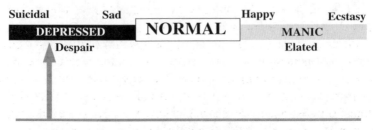

Chemical imbalance prevents the Mood Control Centre from restoring normal mood so thoughts slide into depression.

Figure 3 Mood Disregulation.

14

washing to rid themselves of a sensation of being dirty. This is also known as Obsessive Compulsive Disorder (O.C.D.), see Chapter Twenty One.

There may be a preoccupation with body symptoms and frequent visits to doctors with complaints that can never be diagnosed or treated. Chronic pain is often present and it hides the underlying depression. Medical treatment is then directed at the pain so the mood remains untreated and the emotional disability continues undetected and untreated. Sixty percent of chronic pain patients have a medical depression but they may hide behind the legitimacy of pain to prevent the detection of a less socially acceptable condition.

Socialization is difficult during depression and it becomes very uncomfortable to attend church. Depressed people find that they don't get anything out of church services and often complain that they "aren't being fed". They have multiple complaints about the Pastor or members. It is very common for them to change churches frequently in search of a congregation that will fill their needs.

Crying becomes a frequent event. There is a tendency to blame others, especially spouse, family members or God for their state of unhappiness.

All of the above symptoms by themselves are common and do not always indicate a mental illness. When however, a number of these signs are present continuously for over two months, then treatable illness must be suspected.

The onset of depression is often during the teen years but at that time the symptoms are dismissed as just an "adolescent phase" (see Chapter Seven). Most of my patients have been suffering for over ten years before they realize that help is available. The onset is so insidious that it goes unnoticed and the person and their family just adjust to the changes. It becomes the new normal for that person so they sense no need of corrective treatment.

Depression affects every part of our ability to think and feel. It clouds our personality and changes how we interpret events and how we relate to others. It magnifies physical pain, disrupts relationships, blocks communication and changes our eating and sleeping patterns. It also effects everyone around us in a negative way. There are very few illnesses known, that cut such a broad path of devastation and disability. It is a very common condition but it often goes undiagnosed since there is no confirmatory test and it can be masked by chronic pain, fatigue and burnout.

5

How does Depression affect marriages?

Depression and all mood disorders disrupt relationships both inside and outside the home. Marriages are severely strained by the temper, irritability, fatigue and apathy found in a depressed spouse.

Twenty percent of all marriages are unhappy. In fifty percent of those unhappy couples, one or both spouses have a mood disorder. In my Clinic, the most common cause of marriage failure is a mood disorder in a spouse.

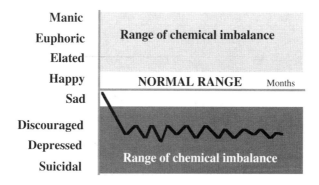

Figure 4 The onset of.depression is insidious and can continue undetected for a lifetime.

6

Does Menopause or Premenstrual Syndrome (P.M.S.) cause Depression?

Menopause has always been blamed for causing depression and has been unkindly referred to as "mental pause". This is not so.

There is no question that mood is affected by the hormonal fluctuations of menopause and of normal menstrual periods. These fluctuations won't however, actually cause a chemical depression. Menopause and P.M.S. tend to magnify the symptoms of a preexisting underlying depression. Unfortunately, when women go to their doctors they usually get treated for only the menopausal symptoms or cyclic bloating and the underlying depression is missed. It is important to treat both the menopausal and depression symptoms separately. They are both biochemical, treatable conditions.

7

Is Adolescent Depression just a normal phase?

Depression and other mood disorders are very common in the teen years and it is estimated that up to twenty percent of teens have depressive symptoms. The rate of suicide in adolescents has risen two hundred percent in the past ten years so it is now the third leading cause of death in that age group. Depression is not a normal developmental phase that will pass. Adolescent mood disorders cause serious disabilities in academic progress and personality development.

Most adult mood disorders begin in adolescence but they are not detected due to the public perception that it is normal for teens to have emotional instability and that "it's just a phase". Frequently a depressed irritable teen will be considered to have "normal youthful rebellion" and then not be considered to have a treatable illness. This is tragic since depressed teens will respond to medications as well as adults do, so they are suffering needlessly. Without treatment, they may have developmental, academic and social problems with lifelong disability.

The teen years are when Attention Deficit Disorder (A.D.D.) children begin to develop mood instability so it is very important to treat them. The symptoms of adolescent depression are the same as in adults, with perhaps a greater degree of irritability, defiance, lack of interest in school and low self esteem. Depressed teens lose the ability to enjoy activities, they change their eating habits, complain of constant fatigue and become worried or withdrawn. They may also show antisocial behaviour with stealing, fighting and trouble with the law. Depressed teens have few friends since they are considered socially undesirable. Many will turn to drugs and alcohol to calm their minds from the constant stream of unpleasant negative thoughts. Addictions are very common in this condition. Families with depressed adolescents are often in constant turmoil and conflict due to the irritability of the teenager.

Adolescent depression is also strongly inherited. Fifty percent of children with depressed parents will also become depressed. Teens respond to the same medications that are used in adults and with the same rate of success. It is very hard however, to convince a teenager or their parents that medications are needed. As a result, the vast majority of adolescent mood disorders remain undiagnosed and untreated, causing years of unnecessary disability and in some cases death.

8

Is it normal for the elderly to be Depressed?

Depression is very common in the later years but it is usually missed and the symptoms wrongly attributed to normal aging.

The incidence of depression increases with age. It is presumed that this is caused by a decline in the level of nerve cell chemicals. This decline seems to be much worse if another unrelated chronic illness is present. Up to thirty percent of stoke victims will become chemically depressed. There is also an increasing level of stress and number of losses in later years which could precipitate depression. The rate of suicide reaches its peak in the elderly age group.

Depression can be easily confused with senility and can be found along with senility. It is important to treat depression as an independent condition since it will respond to treatment at any age.

9

How does Depression affect Christians?

Depression disrupts all relationships including a relationship with God. A depressed Christian will feel that they have lost the joy of their salvation and that they no longer feel God's presence. God will seem farther away, silent and unreachable. It will be very difficult to pray and do devotions since both of these acts require concentration which is disrupted by depression. The victim will be unable to participate fully in worship services since they feel dead inside. At this point many assume that God is punishing them or that they have committed the unpardonable sin. A Christian will then suffer even greater depressive pain since not only do they feel cut off from people but also from God, their last resort for help.

When well meaning Christian friends find out how depressed the person is, they will suggest a greater commitment to prayer and Bible study as a treatment for the condition. This of course, is impossible, since both acts require a great deal of concentration which depression always interferes with. Unfortunately, this inability to pray and study will indicate to the friends that the depressed person must have a spiritual problem, a lack of faith or that they don't really want to get well. Self help books and tapes will then be tried along with perhaps Pastoral counselling. These methods only work when a person has total thought control which allows them to change their thinking patterns. When Christian self help methods fail, the depressed believer will feel so spiritually dead and hopeless that they may give up Christianity completely.

A depressed Christian has additional guilt added to their depression since they usually condemn themselves for not snapping out of it. They will assume that they have a spiritual weakness or a character flaw. Pastors may have taught them that a true Christian will never get depressed and that it is a sign of defeat, disobedience and unbelief, so they feel increasingly guilty. It will be harder to attend church since socialization is very difficult and they feel like hypocrites for not being able to pray, worship of read the Bible. Since concentration is so impaired, they get little out of sermons so they tend to change churches frequently since they "are not being fed" or the church "isn't meeting their needs". Depression is particularly painful for Christians and there is much unnecessary suffering due to their wrong understanding of mental conditions.

Depression appears to be slightly more common in Evangelical churches than in the general population since these churches deliberately attract seekers who are looking for answers to life. Depressed people are always seeking for relief, so many will come into our churches. If the seekers are not helped with their depression as well as with eternal life, there is a very high rate of "backsliding" since they perceive that Christianity has not met their needs and they feel no better.

10

How does Depression affect Pastors?

An untreated depressed Pastor can cause serious damage to a church and to his own ministry. He will likely label his symptoms as "burnout" and may blame it on the congregation, his spouse or superiors. Most often he will blame himself for sliding into a spiritual valley where prayer and Bible study becomes very difficult. When the condition doesn't improve using the usual scriptural methods for drawing closer to God, he then will presume that he is too far from God to be helped and that his "call" or "anointing" has lifted. Pastors are very reluctant to seek help from fellow ministers due to embarrassment, so they suffer in isolation.

If there is mood instability, they may act impulsively and slip into sin. This will then put them under discipline. They will likely then leave the ministry in personal disgrace. This sequence of events can be easily prevented if depression is recognized and treated early.

The Anointing Has Lifted

This Church Is Killing Me

I'm In The Wrong District

I Must Have Sinned

I'm Burned Out

I Can't Pray Or Study

I'm A Total Failure

I Quit

I've Strayed Too Far

11

Why are Christians so difficult to treat?

Mental health problems are poorly understood by the public at large as we have already discussed. The Christian population is not only equally uninformed but we have created our own explanation for the cause and treatments of mental illnesses. It is assumed that since spiritual symptoms are present, then there must be a spiritual cause and that a spiritual treatment will always work. If it doesn't, then the victim is blamed for inadequate faith or motivation. **Christians don't realize that depression is the only medical condition with spiritual symptoms.**

Christians assume that they are in full control of their thoughts but this is not so when a mood disorder is present. One's ability to control thoughts depends on how well the brain cells are functioning to give you that control. It is much like the control of a car. One only has full control if the steering wheel is properly connected

under the hood. In mood disorders, the problem is not with the will of the person but with the nerve cells "under the hood".

Christians are very reluctant to seek medical help with their moods since they perceive that this is an admission that they "don't have enough resources in God" or that "the Cross isn't enough". This is sometimes reinforced by well meaning friends or Pastors who intensify their guilt. It is also thought that no medical treatment could ever help a spiritual problem so it would be an insult to God to accept such treatment.

Christians need to understand that treatment won't undermine their faith nor override their will. Antidepressants are not "mood altering drugs" nor are they addicting. It is quite permissible for Christians to take them. Medications are a part of the recovery process along with Pastoral counselling, praying for healing and personal devotions.

It is my hope that with the information in this book, any pastor or friend will be able to understand depression well enough to know when to recommend that a person seek medical help and to then support the person in the treatment process. Pastors get worn down by the endless counselling required by medically depressed people who rarely show improvement. Using these tools, a Pastor can refer and offer support. He can help the victim understand that this is just another treatable illness. This will give the person a better recovery and will encourage the Pastor rather than exhaust him.

12

What is Manic Depression?

Depression is the most frequent form of mood disorder. The manic depressive or bipolar mood disorder is the next most common. It is characterized by wide mood fluctuations ranging from deep depression and despair to extreme happiness, euphoria and mania.

During a manic phase a person will talk excessively and loudly with words pouring out in an animated continuous stream, interspersed with wit and humour. They will be unable to sit still or relax and there is continuous agitation. They will be distractible, changing topics rapidly, never totally finishing one thought and over committing themselves to any task. Being the "life of the party", they show endless energy, developing grandiose plans based on gross overestimations of their own ability. Their thoughts are continuously racing with exciting plans or jobs to do which demand immediate attention. When opposed they may show intense rage and irritability. They have poor judgment especially when spending money. They need very little sleep and consider rest and eating to be a waste of time only for the weak. During this phase they may act totally out of character and impulsively take risks of a sexual, personal or financial nature. During a "high" they are very reluctant to seek treatment since they feel so great and powerful. Manic episodes are often followed by periods of profound depression which are triggered by the slightest disappointment.

The manic depressive illness can be as successfully treated as depression.

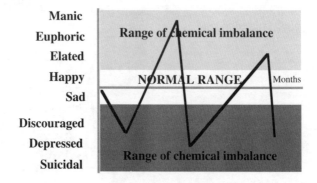

Figure 5 Bipolar illness causes wide mood swings into both ranges of abnormal mood.

13

How can Depression
be treated?

It is important to realize that since depression is an illness, it cannot be fought alone by the victim. It can't be wished away. It needs specific medical treatment to correct the imbalance just like insulin is used to treat diabetes. The most important first step is for the victim to accept the diagnosis and consent to treatment. Even mild chemical depressions can be cleared with medications so there is no need to wait until one is suicidal to begin treatment.

The medical treatment of mood disorders involves the use of drugs which are extremely effective in restoring the normal balance of neurotransmitter chemicals. For depression, there is a family of medications called antidepressants. They restore brain chemistry and correct the imbalance. Concentration, mood and thought control will then be restored (see Figure 6). For bipolar or manic depressives, the mood stabilizing drugs like Lithium, Valproic Acid, or Carbamazapine are used to eliminate and prevent mood swings (see Figure 7).

Most of these medicines have been around for forty years and have an excellent track record for long term safety. They are not habit forming and do not include tranquilizers. They are not "uppers" or "happy pills", they only restore normal mood and the ability to control one's thoughts. They do not create an artificial high nor artificial personality and have no affect at all on a person with normal mood.

It is not possible to know in advance which antidepressant medication will work for any given person. Many may have to be tried for six weeks at a time to find the right one. The benefit of a pill can take six weeks to feel, which is frustratingly slow. I warn everyone that it may take six to eight months to find the right medication that will give maximum benefit with the least side effects. This process is similar to trying to find the right key to open a lock. Many keys may have to be tried before the lock opens. During this waiting period the person needs lots of encouragement to continue trying to find the right medicine.

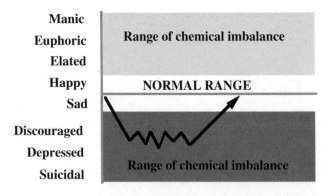

Figure 6 Antidepressants will slowly raise mood by restoring concentration and brain chemical balance.

Once the correct medicine is found, one must stay on it for at least six months after the end of depressive symptoms. This long period lessens the chance of relapse after the medications have been stopped. Statistics have shown that after one episode of depressive illness, fifty percent of recovered people will suffer from another episode within two years. After having two episodes, the risk of relapse within two years increases to seventy percent. It's important that patients recognize the symptoms of relapse early and start treatment as soon as possible. It is generally recommended that the best way to prevent or reduce the risk of relapse is to stay on antidepressant medications indefinitely. For those people who remain on treatment, medications must be considered equivalent to eyeglasses, insulin or heart pills which must be taken for life. These medications are not a crutch but they actually correct the problem as long as they are taken continuously.

Depression can also be seasonal. It usually begins in the Fall and ends in the Spring. This form of depression also responds to medications. Research is currently being done to see if light

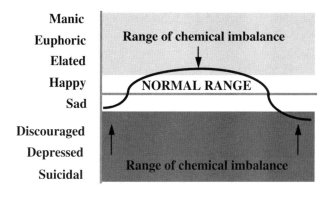

Figure 7 Lithium and other mood stabilizers will normalize mood through restoring brain chemical balance and flattening mood swings.

therapy can help with seasonal depression.

One very often overlooked part of the treatment of depression is the support that is needed for the families of depressed people. These families are living under severe relationship stress and need to understand the illness and how it is treated. They must be helped with the guilt that they carry for having this problem in their family.

Personal and family counselling is a very important part of the treatment. There are usually many scars to heal as a result of psychological trauma and conflict. Counselling works best after the depressed person has regained control of their thoughts and concentration. Friends and counsellors can be very helpful in supporting the person while they are waiting for the medications to work.

Support groups are now widely available for those suffering with emotional disorders. I have found them to be extremely helpful in providing education to the patient and their families. Perhaps their greatest value however, is to provide encouragement to the sufferer to persist with treatment until they have recovered.

With correct treatment, a depressed person can become relaxed, content, optimistic and in full control of their thoughts and behaviors.

14

What is
"Shock Treatment?"

Shock treatment is more properly know as E.C.T., electroconvulsive therapy. It was the original treatment for depression but is now rarely used due to the effectiveness of medications.

E.C.T. is the application of an electric shock to one side of the brain to induce a seizure while the person is safely under general anesthesia. The seizure causes a rapid release of all the nerve cell chemicals which are used to regulate brain function. Some of those chemicals are the ones deficient in depression. The sudden release helps correct the chemical imbalance and restores normal mood. Usually up to ten treatments are required to get the chemicals up to the necessary levels to restore mood. Antidepressant medications are often used to maintain the recovery after E.C.T.

E.C.T. is now generally used only in those who do not respond to medications. It is a safe and rapidly effective treatment. Please don't ever discourage someone from accepting this form of treatment since it could save their lives and minds.

15

What about
Spiritual Warfare?

Spiritual warfare or conflict is a very real issue, especially in depressed Christians. The loss of concentration and the cluttering of negative thoughts make a person particularly vulnerable to occult influences.

When a person's mind is filled with negative discouraging thoughts which can't be shut off, then it is very easy for Satan to insert even more condemning thoughts or suggestions in among the person's own thoughts. The depressed person is unable to detect the intrusion of lies, condemnation or misinterpretations from an evil source and just assumes that the thoughts are his own. The inserted thoughts are intended to magnify the pain of depression and to separate the victim from supportive friends, counsellors and most of all, from God. When concentration is impaired by depression, it is very difficult to "take every thought captive" and block the intrusion of dark thoughts.

This state is much like having a house with no doors or windows covering the holes in the walls. The house is always filling with dirt or debris that is blowing by. It is impossible to keep the house clean. When a mind is racing and cluttered, there is very little defense against evil, disturbing thoughts that are directed against that person. These thoughts will just "blow in" and fill part of the house. A poorly protected mind will accumulate many unwanted negative thoughts, especially the kind which separate a person from God.

When a person recovers from depression, it is much like putting glass and doors over all the holes to keep out unwanted thoughts. In this way, thought control is restored and any thoughts of an evil origin are quickly detected and disposed of. The mind can then be kept clean since the entry points are controlled and monitored.

In my experience, the first step in the process of deliverance or becoming free from the harassment of evil, is to treat any depression that may be present. When thought control and concentration is restored, then believers can use their authority over Satan and he will flee. I strongly recommend the books by Neil Anderson like "The Bondage Breaker", and by Peter Horrobin to help a person learn how to use their authority in deliverance once their mood has been restored.

16

What about the Holy Spirit
and Inner Healing?

Throughout the course of everyone's life, emotional chains or wounds are accumulated as the result of negative events and stresses. These emotional injuries cause personality damage which keeps people trapped in the bondage of negative, destructive thought patterns. The dysfunctional thought patterns interfere with daily activities and damage relationships.

The thought cluttering from mood disorders greatly magnify the disruption caused by these emotional chains. As mentioned in Chapter Fifteen, occult spiritual attacks also keep people chained and resist all their attempts to break free.

At the time of conversion, God accepts everyone as they are, chained, broken and wounded. The Holy Spirit has been provided for Christians to break these chains of the old nature and to heal the wounded personality. This process however, is voluntary. It will only happen if the believer permits it. This is the process of sanctification or refining, which is God's intention for every believer.

Medications can effectively restore thought control and concentration when a mood disorder is present. They do not however, break emotional chains, negative behavioural patterns or occult attacks.

For complete emotional inner healing, God's power is required to break the chains and heal the wounded personality. It is very difficult though, to apply God's truth to your inner self until concentration is restored through the use of medications or divine healing. After this is completed, it is God's intention for the Holy Spirit to complete the task of setting each believer free of their chains. This is accomplished by applying the truth of God's Word with the power of the Spirit.

In 1994 a very powerful outpouring of Holy Spirit power began in Toronto, Canada which has spread internationally through many denominations. It has been known by many names including the "Renewal". I have been personally astonished at the speed that inner healing has taken place in those who have been touched by this Renewal. Emotional chains, negative behaviors and spiritual oppressions have been broken rapidly in many cases. It appears that God has now provided this power for the more rapid rehabilitation of believers rather than the previous lifelong prolonged struggle to break free. This process of inner healing is very essential in the recovery of those who have struggled with emotional chains.

In Figure 8 you will see that there are three links in the chain of emotional bondage. Each link must be addressed if full restoration of the mind and soul is to take place. If any of the three areas are ignored, then recovery will be incomplete. Each area has an affect on the other two areas since they are all interdependent.

The "Chemical Imbalance" link refers to physical causes which result in abnormalities of mood and thought control or concentration.

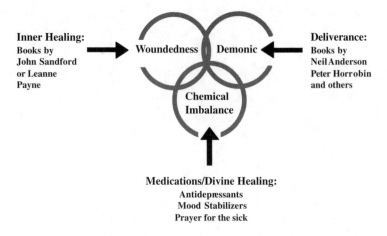

Figure 8 The Chains of Emotional Bondage.

These imbalances must be corrected medically before significant progress can be made in the other two areas.

The "Demonic" link refers to bondage that has resulted from the harassment of evil spirits. This may result from past or present personal sin, being the victim of sin or inherited generational curses. There are many other sources of this kind of bondage. Deliverance is the process of breaking free of the influence of evil spirits that want to influence thoughts and behavior. There are many books and ministries that can help in this area, Neil Anderson and Peter Horrobin are only two of many.

The "Woundedness" link refers to all of the personality damage that has been accumulated during a person's lifetime. These wounds create thought patterns that shape our personality, habits, attitudes and behaviors. Many of these thought patterns are based on lies that have infiltrated our minds without our knowledge. Incorrect attitudes are then formed which influence our behavior and relationships. Inner Healing refers to the process of breaking the emotional chains and healing the wounds that have accumulated from our past. It addresses attitudes, behaviors and relationships.

John Sandford and Leanne Payne are authors who are very gifted in explaining how to recognize woundedness and how the Holy Spirit can set one free. I have seen dramatic results in people who have used the many books from these two authors. There are many other helpful books on inner healing. The best results are usually obtained when you are reading the books recommended by your therapist. Inner healing proceeds much faster when you are working with a Christian counsellor who will guide you in addressing all three links in the chain of emotional bondage.

17

What is A.D.D. or Hyperactivity?

Attention Deficit Disorder (A.D.D.) simply means that a person has a chronic inability to concentrate or focus their mind. It usually presents in one of two ways, with hyperactivity (A.D.H.D.) or without. This is the most common thinking problem in children and it is estimated that six percent of children will suffer from it. It is a leading cause of school failure and underachievement. At least fifty percent of the affected children will never be diagnosed or treated so that they remain disabled, often for life.

The normal brain seems to have filters or gates which allow you to block useless information or stimuli from distracting you from an intended task. In A.D.D. the filters are so weak that the child is bombarded with useless and irrelevant thoughts which are continuously distracting him from learning and remembering. It is very much like being in a small room with many loudspeakers all shouting instructions and not being able to tell which speaker is the important one. The child finds that his brain is telling him too many things at once and he doesn't know how to process all the commands. This causes great frustration which leads to impulsive and socially inappropriate behavior.

This inability to concentrate is caused by an inherited chemical imbalance in the brain, just like the one which causes adult mood disorders. Children have the same racing of thoughts but they are less likely to have the mood symptoms. Their thought clutter is of a more random nature where the adult pattern has more anxious and depressing thoughts. It is very common to find both A.D.D. and mood disorders clustering in families since they are closely related conditions which are both inherited.

There are many symptoms of A.D.D. and not every affected child will have all of them. Children may have any of the following

Attention Deficit Disorder thought patterns

symptoms: not finishing what they start, fidgety, distractible, hearing but not listening, unable to concentrate on school work, making noises in class, falling grades, acting like they are driven by a motor, unable to sit still, loud, always talking and impulsive. They are excitable, unable to share, impatient and demanding of their own way with wide mood swings. In a classroom they appear to be daydreaming or disruptive, unable to apply themselves to a task and easily confused by details. They rarely follow instructions and have exceedingly short memories. There is usually considerable moodiness with extreme emotional responses to events. The irritability, impulsivity and immaturity make it hard for them to make or keep friends so they become socially isolated.

They usually have poor grades since school is such a struggle. They need constant supervision and assistance to complete a task or learn a skill. They are often in trouble with authorities and are automatically blamed for anything that goes wrong. These pressures cause the child to lose all self esteem and feel rejected. They become sullen and withdrawn as they get older. In this way A.D.D. is often seen with depression, anxiety and learning disabilities. Twenty five percent of learning disabled children also have A.D.D.

These children are usually of normal intelligence but they are unable to perform and make use of their abilities. This condition is much like having a high performance sports car ready to go in the garage but having no driveway to get it on the road. There's great potential but no performance.

18

How can A.D.D.
be treated?

Fifty to eighty percent of A.D.D. children are never diagnosed or treated. For those who are identified, the treatment involves a multifaceted approach. I have not found dietary restrictions to be consistently helpful but medications are extremely useful. As in adult mood disorders, the drugs will correct the imbalance and restore normal thought sequence. There are many medications that are helpful including stimulants and antidepressants. Many drugs may need to be tried before the right combination is found though eighty percent of children will respond to stimulants like Methylphenidate (Ritalin). The medications will reduce impulsivity and hyperactivity by slowing down the speed of their thoughts. At a more normal thought speed, it is easier to control thoughts and behavior. Concentration, learning, self confidence and mood will improve as thought control increases. Treatment can release a child from the prison of thought bombardment so that he is able to choose his own thought at his own speed and focus his attention at will.

Parents are generally very reluctant to accept the diagnosis or give pills to their children for this condition. This is very understandable since no one wants to see their child on medications. The fact is however, that with medications the child will be happier and calmer with better performance. This will greatly improve home life and family relationships. I encourage parents to consider Methylphenidate (Ritalin) to be equivalent to eyeglasses or insulin which no parent would deny their child. It must be understood that A.D.D. is a medical problem with behavioral symptoms which will respond to treatment.

The education professionals can be very helpful in tailoring a program for the affected child. Limiting distractions in a classroom and seating the child at the front of the class can be very helpful. Giving instructions frequently and in clear simple terms will help these children respond better. Firm and consistent discipline is necessary though rarely effective if used alone. A.D.D. children need lots of praise and encouragement for the tasks that they do well. Self esteem must be preserved.

Parents are usually exasperated and very embarrassed by their children's behavior which they seem to have no control over. We must reach out to these parents and try to assist them, rather than join the many friends and neighbours who condemn them for poor parenting. Individual and family counselling is very helpful for these troubled families and individuals. Support groups like "Children and Adults with Attention Deficit Disorder" (C.H.A.D.D.) can be a lifeline of help for parents struggling to cope and understand. There are many helpful parenting strategies which can be learned in support groups. Medications are but one of many helpful interventions in A.D.D.

19

What happens if
you don't treat A.D.D.?

It used to be thought that A.D.D. ended in adolescence. It is now known that in forty to sixty percent of cases, the condition continues on into adulthood.

When children with A.D.D. go untreated, they may become sullen with low self esteem, withdrawn, irritable, rebellious and conditioned for failure. They then associate with other kids with the same disability since they are rejected by their peers who can't tolerate their impulsive behavior. In their teens they may become rebellious, defiant and often have trouble with the law. When experimenting with drugs and alcohol, they notice for the first time, that they are able to relax and concentrate until the drink wears off. They then continue to drink because it is the first time in their lives that they have been able to have control of their thoughts. There is a very high incidence of drug and alcohol addiction among untreated A.D.D. and mood disordered adults. Chronic use of these substances will actually make the chemical imbalance worse.

With age, the hyperactive symptoms decline but the mood symptoms increase so there is a very high incidence of depression, anxiety or mania added to the inability to concentrate. Untreated A.D.D. may lead to a lifetime of blame, shame, failure, anger, social isolation, restlessness, underemployment, relationship failure, drug and alcohol abuse and mood disorder. They lead disorganized lives, are forgetful, chronically late, poor time managers, frequently change jobs, homes and spouses. They have severe interpersonal problems due to impulsiveness and intolerance of the opinions of others. This condition affects every aspect of life and personality. I consider it urgent to treat anyone suspected of A.D.D. as soon as the diagnosis is made.

Adults with A.D.D. are often discovered when they bring their own children in for an A.D.D. assessment. At that time the parent recognizes that they too have had the same symptoms their whole life. Adults can be treated with Methylphenidate (Ritalin) but more often with antidepressants and mood stabilizers. Counselling is very important for the adult with A.D.D. since there is usually so much hurt and scarring to overcome before progress can be made.

Treatment will make these people more relaxed, tolerant, dependable, confident, happy with good self control and self esteem.

20

What is
Schizophrenia?

Schizophrenia is not split personality. It is a thought disorder where one loses the ability to tell what is real and what is imaginary. It causes one to hear voices and hallucinate. Schizophrenics often feel that they are being watched, followed or persecuted. This condition is referred to as a psychotic disorder not a mood disorder. It is caused by a different type of chemical imbalance. There is a family of medications to control schizophrenia called antipsychotics.

Antidepressants and mood stabilizers are used if there are many depressive thoughts or wide mood swings along with the psychosis. Antipsychotics are used in mood disorders when the person is also having symptoms of thought disorder along with their mood symptoms.

21

What is Obsessive Compulsive Disorder (O.C.D.)?

Obsessive Compulsive Disorder is quite a common disabling condition. Three percent of the population will suffer from it at some time in their lives. It is more common than Schizophrenia or Manic Depression but it is well concealed and rarely diagnosed.

Obsessional thoughts are recurrent, intrusive, unwanted ideas, images, impulses or worries that are often senseless but can't be shut off. They will often take the form of swear words, repetitive phrases, violent thoughts which are totally out of character or feelings of being dirty or contaminated. This is very disturbing for the victim who feels powerless to control the thoughts. The anxiety associated with O.C.D. can be overwhelming.

Compulsions are repetitive unnecessary acts done in response to the obsessional thoughts. They are intended to neutralize the fear or discomfort that comes with the obsessional thoughts. These acts are purposeless, time consuming and unwanted. They are very disruptive to relationships and to one's performance at home or work. The acts usually involve excessive touching, checking, cleaning, washing, counting or note taking. The victim hates doing it but must continue the act until they get a sense of completion which may require a large number of repetitions. During the compulsion there is never a sense that the action has been completed correctly.

The most common obsessions are fear of contamination by dirt or germs, fear of harm to self or others, fear of illness, fear of sexual thoughts and fear of committing sins. The most common repetitive rituals to suppress the fearful thoughts are repetitive cleaning, recitation of a phrase or number, touching, checking of locks, excessive orderliness and hoarding.

O.C.D. is commonly found with mood disorders and appears to be caused by the same chemical imbalance. It too often begins in childhood or adolescence. The obsessional thoughts are another form of unwanted thought racing and clutter which can usually be controlled by antidepressants.

22

What about Panic, Phobias or Anxiety Disorders?

Anxiety disorders are conditions where one cannot control or stop a sense of continuous worry or fear. Panic is the most severe and disabling form of anxiety disorder. These conditions are very common and have the same incidence and lifetime risk as the mood disorders.

These conditions are commonly found with mood disorders since the continuous anxious thoughts are just another form of negative clutter and racing that can't be shut off. These conditions too, usually respond to antidepressants, often in combination with long acting sedatives.

Tranquilizers are sedatives that temporarily relieve the torment of repetitive anxious thoughts. They do not correct the underlying imbalance but cover it over for a short time. These medicines have generic names that commonly end with the letters "...pam", for example "diazapam". Tranquilizers are useful in the short term treatment of an acute episode of anxiety or mood disturbance. They are commonly used for immediate symptom relief while waiting the several weeks it takes for an antidepressant to take effect. Since tranquilizers can be habit forming, they are usually tapered off as the antidepressant corrects the underlying problem.

As in the mood disorders, medications will help an anxious person regain control of their thoughts so the unwanted thoughts can be shut off.

23

What can be done for Anorexia Nervosa, Chronic Fatigue and Fibromyalgia?

A person suffering from Anorexia is obsessed with unwanted continuous negative thoughts of being too fat. They will be unable to stop worrying about their weight so dieting becomes a compulsion that can't be controlled. Dieting to the point of starvation often takes place since the thoughts won't quit and the victim can never be satisfied that an acceptable weight has been reached.

Thirty to fifty percent of those with Anorexia also suffer from mood disorders since both conditions are caused by a chemical imbalance that allows the mind to race with negative thoughts. Antidepressants can correct the imbalance and restore normal mood and thought control. This will allow the person to accept and restore a normal weight and eating pattern. Counselling is also necessary and helpful with all of these disorders.

The list of symptoms which define Chronic Fatigue Syndrome are very similar to those of depression. Antidepressants can help with the depressive symptoms of the Syndrome so that considerable relief can be obtained.

Fibromyalgia is a condition which among other things, involves chronic muscle pain, sleep disturbance and depression. It is known that sixty percent of those with chronic pain will also have a chemical imbalance depression. The depression can be a result of the chronic pain, or the pain can be a result of chronic depression.

Fibromyalgia will often improve with the use of antidepressants which can improve sleep, relax muscles and give some pain relief. The benefits can be seen even without depressive symptoms being present.

It is easy to see that antidepressants have very wide uses in any condition where unwanted thoughts disrupt concentration or behavior.

Conclusion

It is important for the public to realize that a person with Depression, Mania, Anxiety and Attention Deficit is helplessly in the grip of an illness that they can't control. These conditions are legitimate physical problems with medical treatments just like diabetes or any other chronic illness. It is unfair the way these people are treated with fear, suspicion, hushed embarrassment and condemnation. Most of these people can be totally controlled with medication and returned to a normal productive life. Christians must realize that these are very common treatable physical illnesses which can affect anyone through no fault of their own.

Our communities and churches are full of hurting people looking for answers to life's struggles. Many of them will have mood disorders needing treatment. They are hurt when friends or Pastors declare that depression is a sign of weakness or deficient faith. A depressed person should never be told to "snap out of it" any more than a diabetic should be told to "smarten up and stop using Insulin".

Many are suffering needlessly from depression and other mood disorders. They are unaware that treatment is available and acceptable for Christians. Through public education, more depressed people will realize their need for treatment and they will no longer see themselves as social outcasts. People with mood disorders need to be encouraged to recognize the problem and get help.

This book can help a person diagnose the kind of disorder they have and discover what treatments are available. The Symptoms Checklist in Chapter Twenty Four is a summary of the symptoms of chemical imbalance of mood control. If you are wondering if you or a family member are suffering from a mood disorder, then just compare yourself with the symptoms in the checklist. If you have a number of the symptoms, then take the list to a Physician and discuss how you are feeling, so that a treatment plan can be started.

God has called us to lead our world out of the bondage of sin, let us also minister release to those of our members bound in the captivity of their minds.

Symptoms Checklist

Compare yourself to the symptoms listed below. If they have been present daily for over two weeks, you should take this list to your physician and discuss it with him.

Depression

1. Persistent sad, anxious, or "empty" mood, most of the time most days.
2. Feelings of hopelessness, pessimism and low self esteem.
3. Feelings of guilt, worthlessness, helplessness.
4. Loss of interest or pleasure in hobbies and activities that were once enjoyed, including sex.
5. Insomnia, early-morning awakening or oversleeping.
6. Loss of appetite and/or weight loss or overeating and weight gain.
7. Decreased energy, fatigue, feeling "slowed down" or agitation that can't be controlled. Procrastination, since simple tasks seem harder.
8. Thoughts of death or suicide, suicide attempts, constant feelings of "life isn't worth living like this".
9. Restlessness, irritability, bad tempered, never relaxed or content.
10. Difficulty concentrating, remembering and making decisions due to persistent uncontrollable cluttering of down, sad, negative thoughts that can't be kept out of the mind.
11. Persistent physical symptoms that do not respond to treatment, such as headaches, digestive disorders, and chronic pain.
12. Continuous anxiety which can't be turned off. Worry about smaller things including physical health.
13. Social isolation due to increasing difficulty making small talk.
14. Other relatives with depression, alcoholism or nervous breakdowns.

15. In children look for increased irritability, persisting complaints of physical problems, agitation and extreme unwarranted anxiety or panic.

16. In adolescents look for irritability, drug or alcohol abuse, antisocial, rebellious, defiant behavior, restlessness, truancy from school, poor grades, promiscuity, oversensitivity to rejection and poor hygiene.

Mania

1. Exaggerated elation, rapid unpredictable mood changes.

2. Irritability, impatience with others who can't keep up with them.

3. Inability to sleep, not needing sleep, too busy to sleep and not being tired the next day.

4. Big plans, inflated self esteem, exaggerated self importance, impulsive overspending.

5. Increased talking, louder and faster.

6. Racing and jumbled thoughts, changing topics rapidly, no one can keep up.

7. Increased sexual desire, uninhibited, acting out of character or promiscuous.

8. Markedly increased energy, "can't be stopped", erratic aggressive driving.

9. Poor judgment, no insight, refusing treatment, blaming others.

10. Inappropriate social behavior, brash, telling people off, overreaction to events, misinterpreting events, distortion of meaning of ordinary remarks.

11. Lasts hours to days, usually ending with a crash into profound depression.

Attention Deficit Disorder with Hyperactivity (A.D.H.D.)

1. Racing cluttered thoughts causing constant distraction.

2. Inability to complete tasks.

3. Hearing but not listening.

4. Unable to concentrate on school work unless with one to one attention. Distractible.

5. Making purposeless noises to fill any silence.

6. Falling grades, disruptive in class, defiant of authority, disorganized.

7. Fidgety, in constant motion, acting like being driven by a motor.

8. Unable to sit still, loud, always talking, disruptive and impulsive.

9. Difficulty making or keeping friends, unable to share, demanding their own way, impatient and poor losers.

10. Exaggerated emotional response to both good and bad events with wide mood swings.

11. Unable to follow or remember instructions, daydreaming, not completing tasks.

12. In non hyperactive A.D.D., they will be unable to concentrate but there will be no fidgeting and no excessive movement or loudness. They will usually be described as quiet daydreamers.

13. Other relatives with A.D.D., depression, alcoholism or nervous breakdowns.

For a listing of audio/video tapes of Dr. Mullen's workshops on emotional healing, write to:

Orchardview Medical Media
Box 395
Grimsby
Ontario
Canada L3M 4H8

Fax: 905-945 7770

❖ ❖ ❖ ❖

If you have enjoyed this book and would like to help us to send a copy of it and many other titles to needy pastors in the **Third World**, please write for further information or send your gift to:

Sovereign World Trust, P.O. Box 777, Tonbridge, Kent TN11 9XT, United Kingdom

or to the **'Sovereign World'** distributor in your country. If sending money from outside the United Kingdom, please send an International Money Order or Foreign Bank Draft in STERLING, drawn on a **UK** bank to **Sovereign World Trust**.